Merry Christmas 2017

with love,

The G's

funny ha-ha

Jokes & Riddles from Our Best-Loved Illustrators

Tom Angleberger, Bob Barner, Jaeme Bereal, Harry Bliss,
Randy Cecil, Ashley Despain, Kate DiCamillo, Chris Eliopoulos,
Marla Frazee, Susan Gal, Christy Hale, Rob Harrell, Amy Ignatow,
William Joyce, Fred Koehler, David LaRochelle, Betsy Lewin,
Ted Lewin, Tom Lichtenheld, Constance Lombardo, Aaron Meshon,
Lissa Rovetch, Lane Smith, Raul the Third, Katherine Tillotson,
Maggie Tokuda-Hall, Ursula Vernon, Frans Vischer, Maria van Lieshout,
Jane Wattenberg, Rosemary Wells, Ed Young

CALIFORNIA
BOOKSTORE DAY
MAY 3, 2014

CBD Publishing
San Francisco, California

"**Knock, knock!**"
"Who's there?"
"**Euripides**"
"Euripides who?"
"**Euripides pants and
 you'll buy me new ones!**"

What did the snail riding on the turtle's back say?

Why did the dinosaur cross the road?

It was the chicken's day off.

From a very early age, team sports were very confusing.

A prisoner, after many years, is finally released. He runs around yelling,

"I'm free!
I'm free!"

A little kid walks up to him and says,

"So what,
I'm 4."

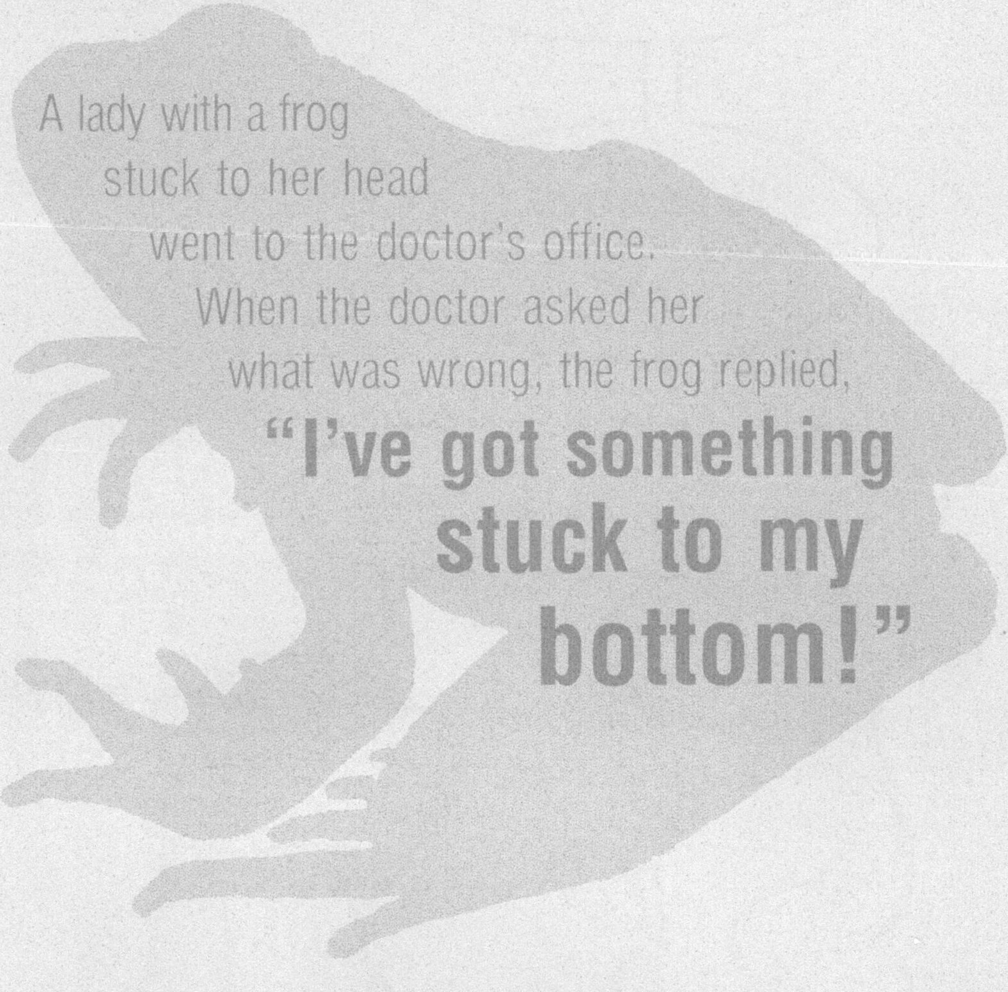

A lady with a frog
stuck to her head
went to the doctor's office.
When the doctor asked her
what was wrong, the frog replied,

**"I've got something
stuck to my
bottom!"**

Illustration by Ursula Vernon

WHEN YOUR FRIENDS ARE TELLING JOKES, HERE'S A GOOD TRICK TO PLAY ON THEM. TELL THEM YOU HAVE A GOOD KNOCK KNOCK JOKE AND QUICKLY ASK SOMEONE TO SAY "KNOCK KNOCK."

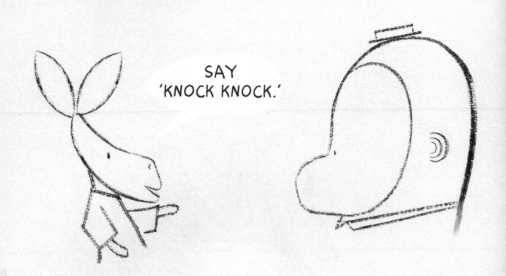

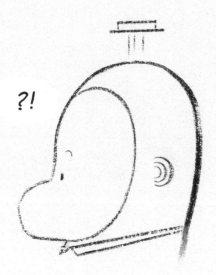

IT GETS THEM EVERY TIME.

Q: What's the difference between a guitar and a fish?

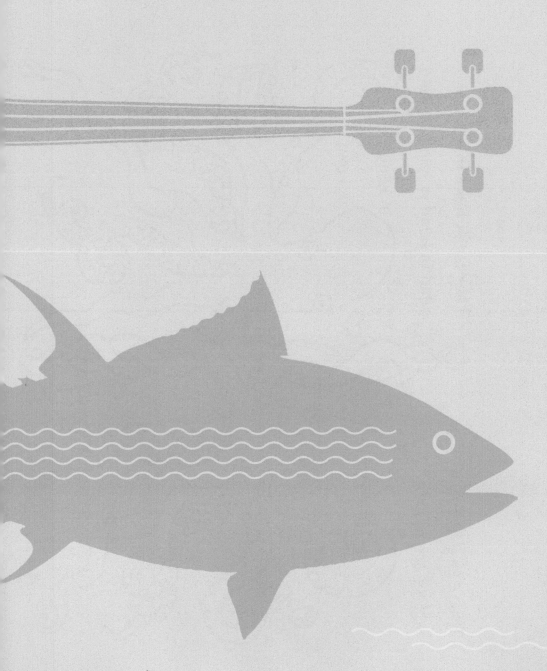

A: You can't tuna fish.

They walk hand in hand in
hand in hand in hand in hand
in hand
in hand

How can you tell if two
octopi are in love?

Illustration by Maggie Toluda Hall

Illustration by Raul the Third

Q: What did the dog get when he multiplied 88 x 7?

A: The wrong answer.

Q: What do you get when you cross a

dog

with an

elephant?

A: A very nervous postman.

Q: What did the alien say to the flower bed?

A: "Take me to your Weeder."

What do you get if you cross a chili pepper, a shovel and a terrier?

One hot-diggity-dog!

" WHAT ABOUT NOW? CAN YOU TELL
I'M HOME NOW?"

Caption by Kate DiCamillo / Illustration by Harry Bliss

WHAT DID THE
MAGICIAN SAY AT
THE FISH MARKET?

"PICK A COD, ANY COD!"

What did
the **bird say**
after his **cage**
fell apart?

Q:What is this dog's favorite city?

A: New **Yorkie**

Two cows were talking in the field.
One cow says,

**"Have you heard about
the Mad Cow disease
that's going around?"**

The other cow answers,

"Yeah, makes you
glad you're a penguin,
doesn't it?"

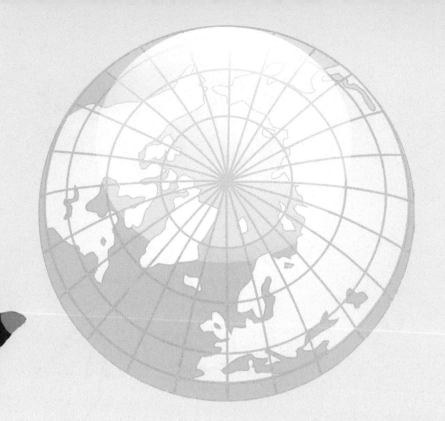

Q: No matter how terrible things get for the people of the Arctic, they will not eat a penguin. Why not?

A: Because penguins live in the Antarctic.

Want to hear a dirty joke?

A white horse fell in the mud.

A horse walks
into a classroom.
The teacher says,
"Why the long face?"

Knock, knock.

Who's there?

Cows go.

Cows go **who?**

No, silly.
**Cows go,
"Moo."**

Q: What do you call a bear with no teeth?

A: A gummy bear.

HEY. CAN YOU STOP? THAT'S *REALLY* ANNOYING.

INTELLIGENCE is understanding that a tomato is actually a fruit;
WISDOM is not using it in a fruit salad.

Illustration by Ed Young

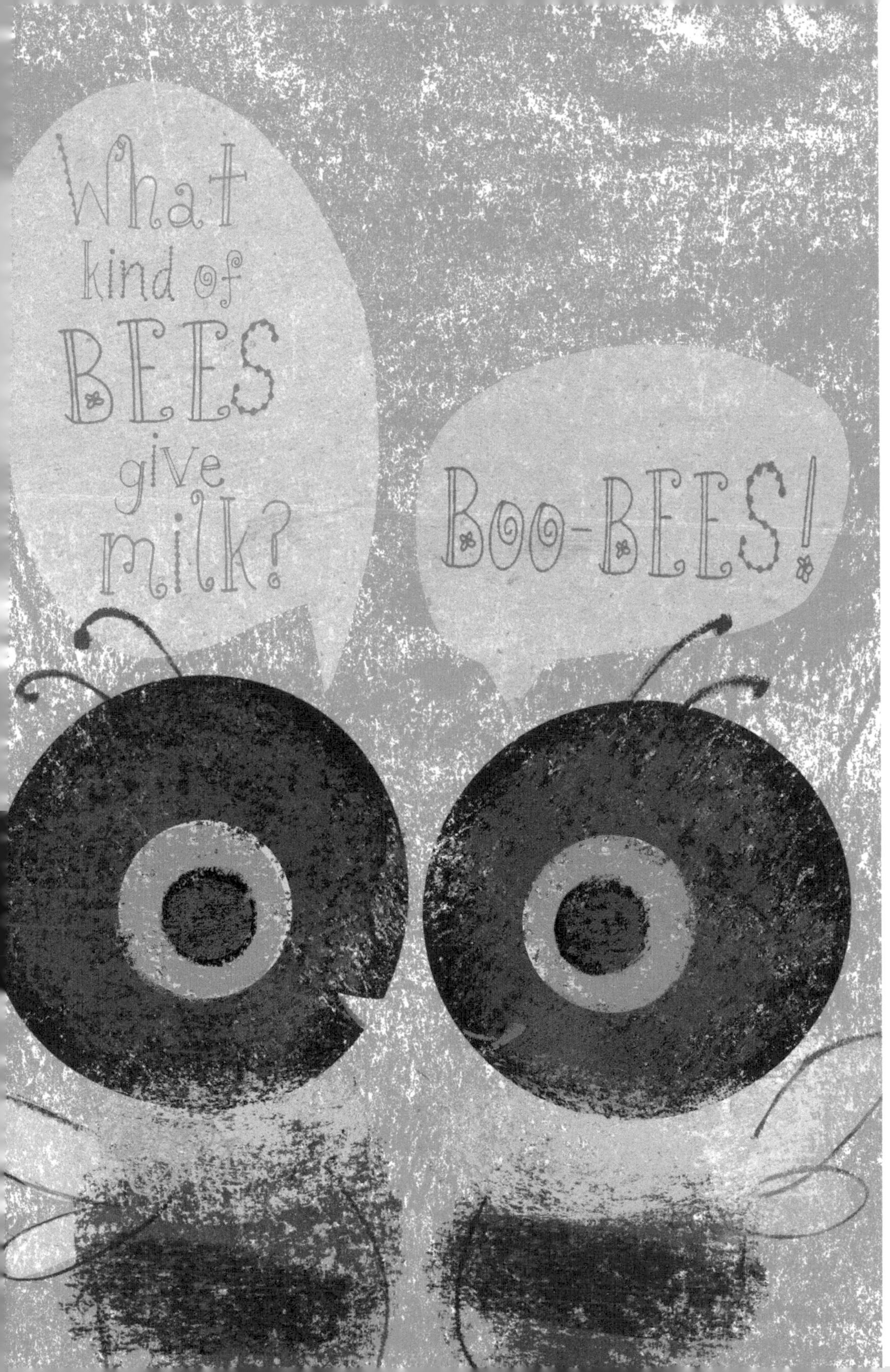
What kind of BEES give milk?
Boo-BEES!

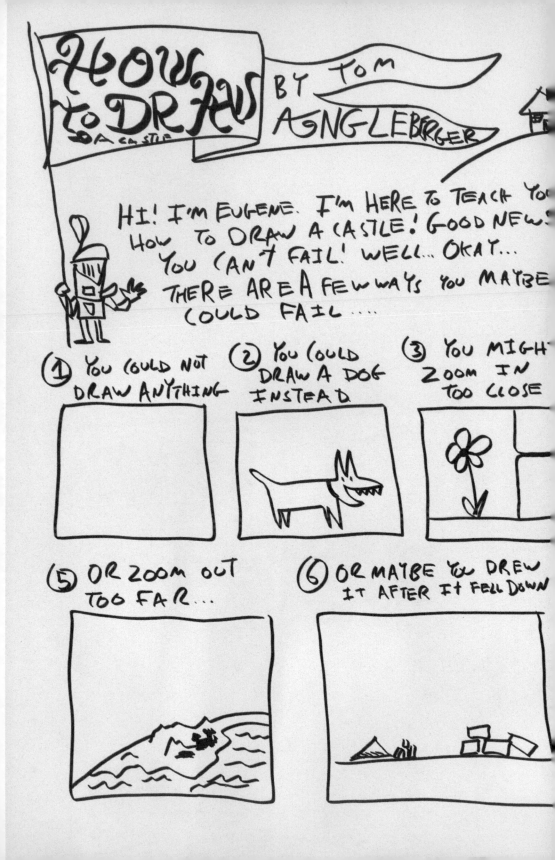

Q: **Why** is a **bad singer** like a **bomb?**

A: Because when you hear her it's too late!

An engineer crosses a road when a frog calls out to him, "If you kiss me, I'll turn into a beautiful princess."

He bends over, picks up the frog and puts it in his pocket.

The frog speaks up again and says, "If you kiss me and turn me back into a beautiful princess, I will stay with you for one week."

The engineer takes the frog out of his pocket, smiles at it and returns it to the pocket.

The frog then cries out, "If you kiss me and turn me back, I'll do whatever you say!"

Again the engineer takes the frog out, smiles at it and puts it back into his pocket.

Finally, the frog asks, "What is the matter? I've told you I'm a beautiful princess, I'll stay with you for a month and do whatever you say. What more do you want?"

The engineer says, "Look, I'm an engineer. I don't have time for a girlfriend, but a talking frog, now that's cool!"

How does a monster
count to 19?

With a calculator!

Why did the kitty cross the road?

To get to the chicken on the other side.

What does it mean if your feet smell and your nose runs?

You're made upside down!

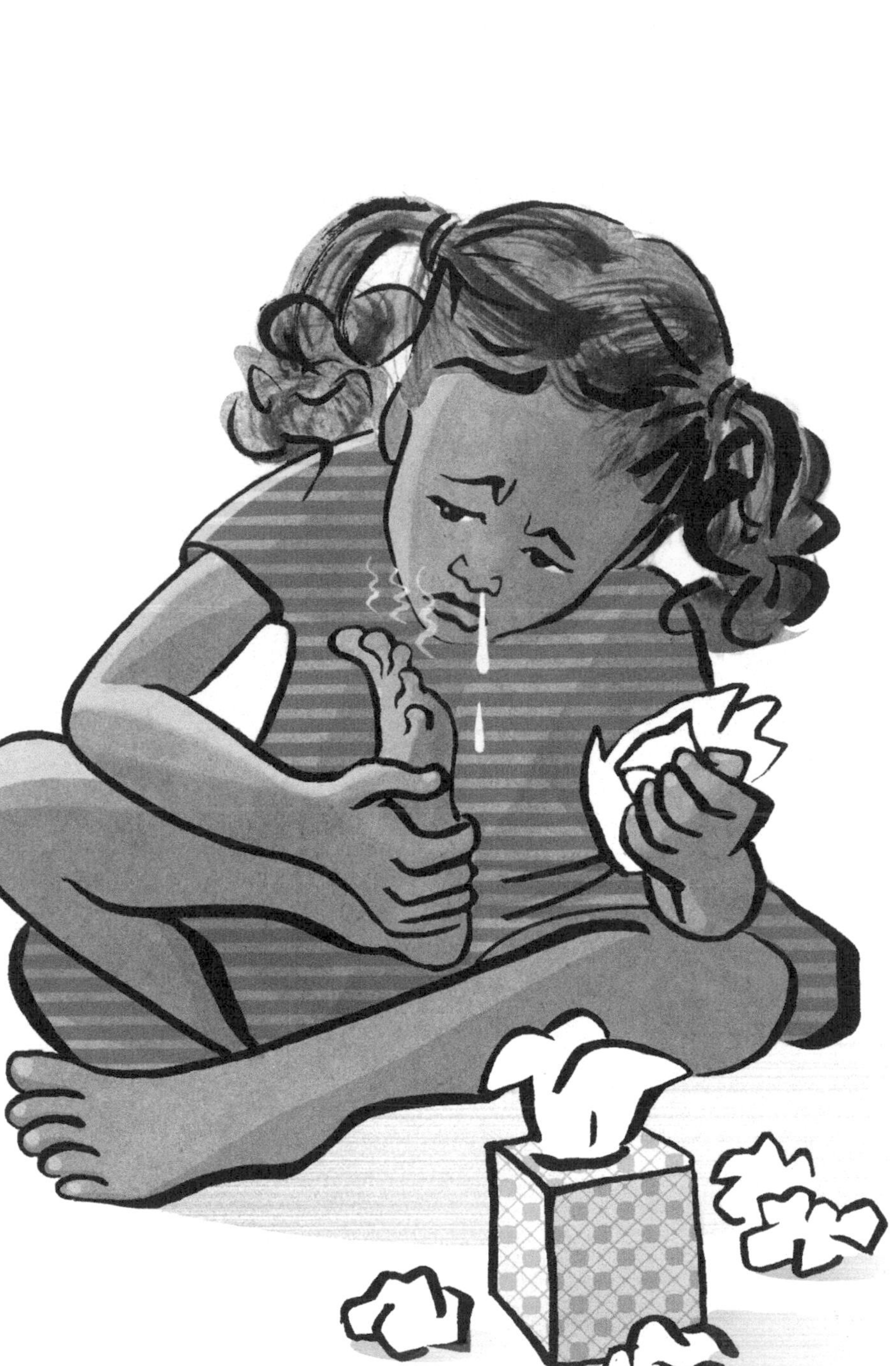

Illustration by Christy Hale

Q: How do you make a tissue dance?

A: You put a little boogie in it.

Q: Why did the ants
dance
on the jam jar?

A: The lid said, "Twist to open."

Bard Grammar

Some English guy named Bill
could never get his fill
of words that worked in rhyme,
he wrote them all the time.

With sonnets, poems and plays,
he filled his working days,
putting wisdom, charm and wit
in every word he writ.

But I wonder; when Bill spoke
or told a corny joke,
or barefoot stepped in slime,
if then his words did rhyme.

Probably not.

Q: What do you get when you cross a giraffe with a hedghog?

A: A six-foot toothbrush.

TOM ANGLEBERGER is the author of the bestselling Origami Yoda series, as well as *Fake Mustache* and *Horton Halfpott*, both Edgar Award nominees, and The Qwikpick Papers series. He lives in Christiansburg, Virginia, with his wife, the author-illustrator Cece Bell. Visit him online at **origamiyoda.com**.

BOB BARNER is the creator of many popular children's books including *Dem Bones*, *Bugs! Bugs! Bugs!* and *Fish Wish*. He likes to present his work to schools and libraries all around the world. He loves to play his guitar and tell jokes in his spare time. **bobbarner.com**

"A silly idea will tickle my funny bone, then an illustration may bloom." **JAEME BEREAL** has completed the children's book *In Her Hands: The Story of Artist Augusta Savage*, and book cover for Deborah Santana's memoir *Space Between The Stars*, as well as award winning illustrations. She graduated from both UC Berkeley and Academy of Art University. Please look for her on line at **jaemebereal.com**.

HARRY BLISS is the *New York Times* bestselling artist and author of his many books including *Diary of a Worm*, *Diary of a Spider*, and *Diary of a Fly*, by Doreen Cronin; *A Fine, Fine School* by Sharon Creech; *Which Would You Rather Be?* by William Steig; and *Louise: The Adventures of a Chicken* by Kate DiCamillo. He is also an award-winning, internationally syndicated cartoonist and a cover artist for the *New Yorker* magazine. He lives in Vermont with his son. **harrybliss.com**

RANDY CECIL has illustrated more than twenty books for children, including *Brontorina* by James Howe, and the *New York Times* bestseller, *And Here's To You!* by David Elliott. He is also the author-illustrator of *Duck and Gator*. Randy lives in Houston, Texas. **randycecil.com**

ASHLEY DESPAIN is a mild-mannered purveyor of kids books by day, but at night dons a cape and mask to become a crime-fighting superhero. He lives in a fortified compound in the heart of San Francisco, surrounded by a moat filled with grumpy cephalopods that have a penchant for accordianomics. Most of his illustrations are based on personal experiences, so he keeps his costume handy at the bookstore, you know, just in case.

KATE DICAMILLO is currently the National Ambassador for Young People's Literature and the author of many books for young readers. Her books have been awarded the Newbery Medal (*The Tale of Despereaux*, 2004 and *Flora & Ulysses*, 2014), the Newbery Honor (*Because of Winn-Dixie*, 2001), the *Boston Globe* Horn Book Award (*The Miraculous Journey of Edward Tulane*, 2006), and the Theodor Geisel Medal and Honor (*Bink and Gollie*, co-author Alison McGhee, 2011; *Mercy Watson Goes for a Ride*, 2007). **katedicamillo.com**

CHRIS ELIOPOULOS began his illustration career as a letterer for Marvel, and has worked on thousands of comics, including *Franklin Richards: Son of a Genius*, *Pet Avengers*, and *Cow Boy*, all of which he wrote and illustrated. He is the illustrator of the *New York Times* bestselling Ordinary People Change the World series of picture book biographies which includes *I Am Rosa Parks*, *I Am Amelia Earhart*, and *I Am Albert Einstein*. **chriseliopoulos.com**

MARLA FRAZEE was awarded a Caldecott Honor for *All the World* and *A Couple of Boys Have the Best Week Ever*. She is the author-illustrator of *Roller Coaster*, *Walk On!*, *Santa Claus the World's Number One Toy Expert*, *The Boss Baby*, *Boot & Shoe*, and her newest *The Farmer and the Clown*, as well as the illustrator of many other books including *The Seven Silly Eaters*, *Stars*, and the *New York Times* bestselling Clementine series. Marla teaches at Art Center College of Design in Pasadena, California, has three grown sons, and works in a small backyard cabin under an avocado tree. **marlafrazee.com**

SUSAN GAL began her illustration career as a poster and calendar artist. Her lively and whimsical illustrations have appeared in magazines, newspapers, books, and on the silver screen. She is the author of *Night Lights*, a *School Library Journal* Best Book of the Year, *Please Take Me for a Walk*, *Into the Outdoors*, and *Day By Day*, a *Kirkus Reviews* Best Children's Book of the Year. She lives with her family in Berkeley, California. You can see more of Susan's work at **galgirlstudio.com**.

RAUL THE THIRD is an artist from El Paso/Juarez. His work is in the collections of the Museum of Fine Arts, Boston, the Fitchburg Art Museum, New Hampshire Art Museum and many private collections. He is currently working on the second volume of *Lowriders in Space* and SpongeBob Comics. He teaches classes on drawing and comics for kids at the Museum of Fine Arts and the Institute of Contemporary Art. He lives in Medford, Massachusetts. **raulthethird.com**

CHRISTY HALE wears designer, art director, illustrator, and author hats. She has illustrated over twenty award-winning titles, including the Elizabeti series and also written *The East-West House: Noguchi's Childhood in Japan* and *Dreaming Up: A Celebration of Building*, a *Boston Globe* Horn Book Nonfiction Honor Award recipient. **christyhale.com**

ROB HARRELL writes and illustrates the Life of Zarf series, the story of a seventh grade troll trying to survive life, royal classmates and the occasional dragon attack in a storybook middle school. **robharrell.com**

AMY IGNATOW is a cartoonist and the author of *The Popularity Papers, a* series of scrapbook-style illustrated novels. She is a graduate of Moore College of Art and Design and lives in Philadelphia with her husband, Mark, their daughter, Anya, and their cat, Mathilda, who is mostly very terrible. **amyignatow.com**

WILLIAM JOYCE makes films and apps but children's books are his true bailiwick (*The Guardians of Childhood*, *The Numberlys* and *The Fantastic Flying Books of Mr. Morris Lessmore*, also an Academy Award®-winning short film). He lives with his family in Shreveport, Louisiana, where he works with his team at Moonbot Studios. **williamjoyce.com**

FRED KOEHLER eats oatmeal because it's good for him, not because he likes it. When he's not mucking about on the coast of Florida or hanging with his two incredible kids, Fred writes and/or illustrates books like *How to Cheer Up Dad*, *One Day, The End*, and *Super Jumbo*. Visit him at **freddiek.com** or follow him on social media **@superfredd**.

DAVID LAROCHELLE has been creating books for young people for over twenty-five years. His recent picture book titles include *It's a Tiger!*, *How Martha Saved Her Parents from Green Beans*, and the one-word book *Moo!* He lives in White Bear Lake, Minnesota, where he enjoys carving creative pumpkins which you can view at his website **davidlarochelle.com**.

BETSY LEWIN wanted to be an artist from an early age. As a child, the illustrators A.B. Frost and Ernest Shepard were among her earliest heroes. The styles of James Stevenson and Quentin Blake have influenced her own children's illustrations. After college she began writing and illustrating stories for children's magazines. When a publisher asked her to expand one of her stories into a book, she jumped at the chance. Betsy has many best-selling books and has been awarded a Caldecott Honor for *Click, Clack, Moo: Cows That Type* by Doreen Cronin, and a Theodore Geisel Honor for *Cowgirl Kate & Cocoa*. **betsylewin.com**

TED LEWIN always knew he wanted to be an illustrator. When it came time to fund his art school education, he took a summer job as a professional wrestler—the beginning of a fifteen-year part-time career that inspired his autobiographical book *I Was a Teenage Professional Wrestler*. Ted's career as an artist began with illustrations for adventure magazines, but over the last thirty-five years he has devoted full time to writing and illustrating children's books. Among his many accolades, Ted was awarded a Caldecott Honor for his illustrations in *Peppe the Lamplighter*. **tedlewin.com**

TOM LICHTENHELD's career in children's books was a happy accident. Drawing a book for his nephew, he ended up creating twenty pages of silly pictures and nonsense about pirates. It became his first book, *Everything I Know About Pirates*. Since then, Tom has continued to draw pictures and make up stories. He is the illustrator of the bestseller *Goodnight Goodnight, Construction Site* and the co-author and illustrator of *Shark vs. Train*. **tomlichtenheld.com**

CONSTANCE LOMBARDO began drawing when she was ten years old, inspired in part by the Illustrators Annuals her dad brought home from the ad agency where he worked. She received her BFA in Illustration from Syracuse University and has had illustrations in a variety of magazines. Her debut illustrated middle grade novel, *Mr. Puffball: Stunt Cat to the Stars* is coming out this fall. She is represented by Lori Nowicki of Painted Words. Plus she likes cats.

AARON MESHON illustrates for editorial, advertising, products, and books around the world. Aaron's first book, *Take Me Out To the Yakyu* was on the *New York Times* top 100 of 2013. His second children's book, *Tools Rule!* was released in 2014. Aaron dreams of selling his products from a small sweet potato truck in rural Japan, but for now Aaron lives with his wife and their French bulldog, Chubu in Brooklyn, New York. **aaronmeshon.com**

LISSA ROVETCH had made pictures and words for lots of silly books like *Ook the Book*, Trigwater Did It, *Hot Dog and Bob*, and *There Was a Man Who Loved a Rat and Other Vile Little Poems*. Next to her world famous cod fish collection, laughter is her favorite thing. **lissarovetch.com**

LANE SMITH is a four-time recipient of the *New York Times* Best Illustrated Book award and a two-time Caldecott Honor recipient. In 2012, he was named a Carle Artist by the Eric Carle Museum for "lifelong innovation in the field of children's picture books." In 2014, he was awarded a lifetime achievement award from the Society of Illustrators. Some of his books are: *It's a Book*, *Grandpa Green*, and *John, Paul, George & Ben*. He also likes squirrels. **lanesmithbooka.com**

KATHERINE TILLOTSON grew up in Minnesota and kept moving west until she reached San Francisco. She has illustrated many books, including *Shoe Dog*, *It's Picture Day Today* and *All the Water in the World*. She lives in a house on a hill with her husband and two dogs. Find more of Katherine's books and illustrations at **katherinetillotson.com**

MAGGIE TOKUDA-HALL is a lifelong reader and was a long time children's bookseller. Her debut picture book, A*nd Also an Octopus*, will come out in 2016. Her favorite places all have lots of books and her favorite people all read them. You can learn more about her at **prettyokmaggie.com**

URSULA VERNON lives in North Carolina and writes and draws the series *Dragonbreath* and *Hamster Princess*, as well as the books *Castle Hangnail* and *Nurk*. She has a husband, a defective beagle, and her favorite joke is the one about the three-legged pig. **ursulavernon.com**

When **FRANS VISCHER** was eleven years old his family emigrated from Holland to America. Speaking no English, Frans' drawings helped him communicate. When he was thirteen, Frans' family visited the Disney Studio, where he was encouraged to make his own animated films. In 1981, the Walt Disney Company hired Frans. He has worked on films such as "Who Framed Roger Rabbit?" and "The Princess and The Frog." His books include *Jimmy Dabble*, *Fuddles*, *A Very Fuddles Christmas*, and the forthcoming *Fuddles And Puddles*. Frans, his wife, and three kids live in Glendale, California. **fransvischer.com**

MARIA VAN LIESHOUT was born and grew up in a small town outside Amsterdam. After completing high school in

Holland, she graduated from The George Washington University in DC with a BFA in Visual Communications, and worked as Creative Director for Coca-Cola in Rotterdam and Atlanta. After she won the green card lottery, Maria left corporate life to write and illustrate books for kids. She lives in a creaky 107-year old apartment in San Francisco with her husband and their son. **mariavanlieshout.com**

JANE WATTENBERG is the author/illustrator of many eye-popping photo-collage books for children. The NY Times squawked, "Yowza!" for her hip-hop adaptation of *Henny-Penny*. Her *Never Cry Woof!* has so much "high octane fun" that it won a Children's Choice Award. Jane's accordion books for babies, *Mrs. Mustard's Baby Faces* and *Mrs. Mustard's Beastly Babies* are celebrating 25 years in print. Her photo-illustrated, *The Duck and the Kangaroo*, written by Mr. Edward Lear, is a lush and roo-mantic love song. Jane lives on a hill in San Francisco where she raises chickens and goats, ducks and bees. **janewattenberg.com**

ROSEMARY WELLS' career as an author and illustrator spans more than forty years and 120 books. She has won numerous awards, and has given readers such unforgettable characters as Max and Ruby, Noisy Nora, and Yoko. She has also given Mother Goose new life in two definitive editions, and created an unforgettable world for grown-ups and kids alike in *Voyage to the Bunny Planet*. **RosemaryWells.com**

Caldecott Medalist **ED YOUNG** is the illustrator of over eighty books for children, seventeen of which he has also written. He finds inspiration for his work in the philosophy of Chinese painting. Born in Tientsin, China, Ed Young grew up in Shanghai and later moved to Hong Kong. As a young man, he came to the United States on a student visa to study architecture but turned instead to his love of art. **edyoungart.com**

California Bookstore Day Publishing
A division of California Bookstore Day and
The Northern California Independent Booksellers Association
The Presidio, P.O. Box 29169 San Francisco, CA 94129-0169
cabookstoreday.com indiebookstoreday.com

MAY 2   2015

INDEPENDENT
BOOKSTORE
DAY

Acknowledgments
Independent Bookstore Day would like to thank
all the authors and illustrators who generously donated
the work herein to benefit indie bookstores
and their young readers.